D1081765

A Bath For Gus

by Jeannette Sanderson
Illustrated by Rebecca Thornburgh

SCHOLASTIC INC.
New York   Toronto   London   Auckland   Sydney

"Come in, Gus!" I call.

My dog runs to me.

I pick him up.

Oh, no!

There is mud on Gus.
There is mud all about!

"You need a bath," I say.

Gus jumps down and runs.
That pup is fast!

"Bad dog! Stop!" I call.
But Gus will not stop.

5

I hunt for Gus.

Where is that pup?

What is that big lump?
There he is!

Oops!

That is not Gus.

This is Uncle Bud.

I see mud.
I think I see a thick tail.
Is that where Gus went?

8

Yes!

Now I have got you!

What is this thing?

This is a mop, not Gus.

Where is Gus?

Where can that pup be?

Is he under the bed?

I toss him his stick.

Gus runs out.
I grab him.

"Now I have got you!" I say.

I fill up the tub.

Gus is under the rug.

What can I do about Gus?

I think about it.

There is one thing left to do.

I get in the tub.
I flip and flop all about.
I fill a cup with suds.
"Rub-a-dub-dub!
This bath is fun!" I say.

And Gus jumps in!

Phonics Reader 12 ★ Words to Sound Out

/u/ *u*	/th/ *th*	-un
up	that	fun
uncle	then	hunt
under	thick	runs
Bud	thing	
but	think	
cup	this	
Gus	bath	
jumps		
mud		
nuts		
pup		
rub-a-dub-dub		
rug		
suds		
tub		

Phonics Reader 12 ★ Words to Remember

about   be   now   then   will

Phonics Reader 12 ★ Story Words

do   need   oh   say